FOR GOD'S SAKE DOCTOR

by
Frances McAll

First published in 1984 by
Grosvenor Books, 54 Lyford Road, London SW18 3JJ
21 Dorcas Street, South Melbourne, Victoria 3205,
Australia
PO Box 1834, Wellington, New Zealand

ISBN
0 901269 82 4 paperback

Cover Design: Cameron Johnson

PHOTOTYPESET BY INPUT TYPESETTING LTD LONDON
SW19
PRINTED BY BIDDLES OF GUILDFORD

Contents

ACKNOWLEDGEMENTS

My thanks are due to all those friends, colleagues and family who have helped by suggestion or criticism with the writing of this book and to the patients, none of whom is mentioned by name, who so willingly gave their permission for me to use their stories.

Above all I would like to acknowledge the debt I owe to the Oxford Group, now better known as Moral Re-Armament, who provided me with the key to faith and a continuing stimulus to put it into practice.

Trust in the Lord with all your heart.
Never rely on what you think you know.
Remember the Lord in everything you do
and He will show you the right way.
Never let yourself think you are wiser than you are;
simply obey the Lord and refuse to do wrong.
If you do, it will be like good medicine,
healing your wounds and easing your pains.

Proverbs 3

1

Introduction – Author's Case History

From the age of seven medicine seemed to me to be the only goal worth aiming at. Once I discovered that even girls could be doctors, no doll was safe. My sister possessed an outsize doll called Violet who was an ideal subject for operations and was remarkable for the number of appendixes she grew and re-grew. Apart from amputation, which was reserved for the more decrepit stuffed dolls, this was the only operation we knew about.

Problems arose when more than one of us wanted to be the surgeon. I already felt, by some inherited instinct, that doctors were superior to nurses. It was a definite climb-down to be the one who had to hold the scissors or pass the cotton wool to mop up the red paint.

Our family doctor at that time was a tall, grey, softly-spoken Scot with humorous eyes and comforting hands. I imagined myself as his female counterpart, not in the humble sphere of general practice, but moving from bed to bed in a large hospital ward while patients gazed up at me with gratitude and devotion. As I grew up, possibly through the influence of various missionaries who stayed in our home from time to time, this vision shifted away to more exotic areas in Africa or China. It became an accepted fact that I would one day be a medical missionary.

This idea was rudely shattered in my teens when I began to question everything, particularly God. The church we attended seemed irrelevant and I was irritated by the old ladies who sat in the same pew week after week. Though I began to doubt God's existence, I couldn't push Him out of my mind. The need to find the truth became more and more urgent.

It never occurred to me to confide in my mother or father or in anyone else for that matter. We were not in the habit of telling each other what we thought or felt. I could not bring myself to tell them that I might change my mind about my career. I feared the shock might be too great for them and certainly too uncomfortable for me. The only thing I could do was to carry on and hope that in the general business of a medical missionary's life, no one would notice whether I believed in God or not. After all, it would be an interesting and useful job.

At this point God Himself intervened. Three young men, part of a group which had been invited to hold meetings in our church, came to stay with us. I do not remember much about the meetings except that they were the first religious ones I had ever enjoyed. What I do remember is the morning when one of our visitors came down to breakfast looking remarkably cheerful and announced that God had woken him at six o'clock. My father looked slightly shocked at this apparent familiarity with the Almighty, but I felt a sudden strange surge of hope. For these people at least, God was not just a doubtful ideal but someone close at hand, recognisable and knowable.

I felt I would do anything to be as sure as they were, so sitting on the edge of my bed with a pencil poised hopefully in my hand as they had suggested, I made a shaky start. I asked Him to tell me if there was anything getting in the way of my finding Him. The response was immediate and unexpected. I suddenly saw what a self-righteous, critical person I was. The good opinion of myself which I thought others shared was rudely shattered in a matter of seconds. The odd thing was that I did not feel rebuked or condemned but as if a light had been switched on – a searchlight which made me want to blink and turn away and yet want to be different.

There were things I would have to put right, such as the jealousy I felt towards my sister who was more popular than I was. Telling her about this opened floodgates of confidence which have never been closed. There were more difficult things about which I could do nothing except ask God's forgiveness. Yet I felt blanketed by a warmth of love I had never imagined possible. God for me became Jesus Christ, worker of miracles and personal friend.

After this experience, I had no further doubts about what I should do. Edinburgh had long been the medical school of my dreams and in those days, provided you had the necessary qualifications, there was little difficulty about getting in. At that time women medical students were very much in the minority, but were given equal treatment to the men in all departments except clinical surgery. Here it was still considered unsuitable for us to watch operations in the same theatre. This may have been out of consideration for our female susceptibilities. After one particularly unpleasant operation, the surgeon looked around at us all sitting in the gallery. He carefully counted and, finding no one missing, said with a smile, "Congratulations, ladies." From then on, having proved our toughness, we were integrated with the men.

It was during this time that I met Ken. He too was a medical student and was bound for China as a missionary. We were to get married in Peking seven years later. Meanwhile he qualified and went off, leaving me to finish as soon as I could.

Medicine in the thirties, especially outside hospitals, left much to be desired. As a final year student I was called out with my partner, in the middle of the night, to attend a woman in labour. It was a long cycle ride and by the time we reached the ancient tenement building the baby had arrived. It was lying uncovered on a sodden sheet of newspaper. A small coal fire burned smokily in the grate. The middle of the room was occupied by a pram covered with a large red tablecloth. As I was cutting the umbilical cord, my eye caught a movement from the pram as a small head pushed up the tablecloth and rapidly disappeared again. There were no clothes for the new baby. The neighbour, who had come in to help, had to go upstairs to fetch a skirt of her own to wrap it in.

Things were not very different in East London where, at the beginning of 1939, I launched into my career as a locum for a sick GP. There was no National Health yet, only a panel scheme for those people lucky enough to be employed. The rest had to do the best they could and many went without.

The doctor's consulting room was lined with shelves full of little bottles with Latin labels but these were merely museum specimens. The real work was done by eight large bottles standing on a dusty card table behind a screen in the corner of the room. There was one for indigestion, others for diarrhoea, constipation and anaemia. There was a cough mixture, a sedative and something to bring down temperatures. What more could one want? The room was never cleaned as the aged housekeeper was afraid to move the piles of unopened advertisements, periodicals and samples which covered every available space.

One of my patients was an old woman who lived alone. She had severe bronchitis. After I had listened to her rattling chest and written a prescription, she pulled a grubby little purse out from under her pillow, extracted two shillings and begged me not to call again unless she sent for me – the cost was more than she could afford. Many doctors in those days treated people for nothing, rewarded only by the occasional cabbage or packet of tea, plus, of course, goodwill.

It was while I was in East London that I met

Annie, a small wiry person in her sixties in whose presence it was impossible to feel depressed. But it hadn't always been so. She came from a background of poverty and resentment and had suffered for years with arthritis. One day eighteen months earlier, she told me, she had decided to drop her bitterness and let God do what he liked with her for the rest of her life. She showed me her gnarled hands and said that she had just realised that very morning that there had been no pain in them or any other joint since. She had become so involved in caring for other people she hadn't even noticed the miracle. It was the first time I had seen such a thing happen.

Later that year, just before the outbreak of World War II, I set off for China and Ken. The journey took four months. The first boat dumped its passengers in Bombay after being ordered home to act as a troop carrier. The second boat was sunk by a mine in Singapore harbour, taking all my personal belongings and our wedding presents with it. The third one narrowly survived a typhoon in the South China Sea.

During the sinking off Singapore, I experienced a great sense of calm in spite of the panic all around. I thought, "Whether I live or die is God's affair." Underneath I was aware of a sneaky pride at how well I was taking the whole thing. It was a hot, sunny morning, the sea was calm and I was a good swimmer. The thought of sharks did not enter my mind.

The typhoon was another matter. As I clung to my bunk, while the ship made up its mind whether to return to the horizontal or not, I learned what it was to be frightened. In a sea like that there could be no escape. When it was over there was little room for anything but thankfulness for life and the resolution to make the most of what I had been given.

Then followed two years of the kind of work we imagined we would be doing for the rest of our lives. Japan had invaded China in 1937 and now held the railways, and the towns and cities along them. Away from the railway it was a different matter. Around the village where I joined Ken, the Japanese and Chinese Communist guerillas constantly fought each other. My first task was to learn the language so that I could work with Ken in the village hospital.

When life and work became impossible for us there, we moved to Cheloo University in the ancient city of Jinan in Shantung province. We were invited to take on the health care of the students and staff, a job created for us and, from our point of view, ideal. In the summer of 1941 our first baby was born. Already there were rumblings of war and, sure enough, at the end of the year World War II caught up with us as Japan came into the war on the side of Germany. We were now not only undesirable aliens but enemy ones, and normal life came to a full stop. We spent the next four years behind barbed wire in a succession of internment camps.

These years in camp gave us what was perhaps the most valuable education of our lives. We learned how to live with hundreds of other people of all types, colours and ages, cooped up in a small space with little to do, a minimum of food and a very dubious future. We were plagued by bed-bugs in summer, by rats all the year round and shrivelled up by cold in the winter. We had the anxiety of seeing our little girl ill when we had no proper medicine to give her, while raindrops dripped from the ceiling. We witnessed human nature in the raw as people fought, gossiped or refused to speak to each other.

The only privacy to be found in the camp was in the hospital. Here people came to unload their fears and frustrations. Then they began to meet secretly with us in the early mornings, to ask God to tell us how to deal with the problems of the camp. As we put the resulting ideas into practice, the community was gradually transformed and democracy began to develop. As their feeling of security and purpose grew, people began to share their closely guarded possessions and varied talents. Fear and frustration lost their grip. It would take another book to tell all that happened during those years, but we came home after the war certain that if such changes could happen under those circumstances, they could happen anywhere.

We returned to post-war Britain thinner but wiser. By now I was expecting our second child and, with no immediate prospect of returning to China, we decided to put up a plate at our front gate and try settling down in general practice. It was the year before the National Health Service started.

Many of the problems which presented themselves over the next ten years were at root the same as we had met in the camp. Ken decided to study psychiatry so as to be better equipped to deal with them. After several years working in psychiatric hospitals, while I coped with the practice, he decided to go into private practice in order to have the time he felt he needed for his patients. Eventually, as patients coming from a distance began to stay with us, we were obliged to register as a Nursing Home. I now became Matron, in fact if not in name. Some patients stayed for a few days, others for several years. Many became close friends.

Meanwhile the family continued to grow and demand my attention. It is often said that women doctors want the best of both worlds – their home and their profession. This I certainly had as I scrubbed floors, washed nappies, cooked meals and, whipping off my apron, dealt with the patients who turned up at the door or were living in the house. When all five children went to school I was able to settle down to more regular part-time work in general practice.

This hybrid existence has convinced me that health and relationships frequently break down because people feel trapped by their own character and behaviour, or by other people's. They do not know that God's wisdom and love are available to all of us and can transform our lives if we let them.

The following chapters describe some of the experiences of patients, friends and family which lie behind this conviction.

2

Under My Skin

"For God's sake, doctor, give me a tranquilliser or I shall go round the bend!" she said as she flung herself down on a chair. She was the last patient that evening and I was just thinking how nice it would be to be finished.

Of the two alternatives she offered, a tranquilliser certainly seemed the better, so I picked up my pen to write a prescription. At the same time I knew very well that this by itself was no cure for her ills. I would give it to her now and ask her to come back again when I hoped I would feel more like tackling her problems. There are times when one can feel an actual dislike for a patient who is inconsiderate enough to present one with problems for which there are no easy answers.

As I was poised to write, something stopped me. It was as though someone was saying to me, "Find out now what the trouble is." It was the usual story. Her husband didn't understand her, she felt there was a wall between them, they could no longer speak to each other and, of course, it was all his fault. She

16

was on edge, sleeping badly, eating too much and unable to concentrate.

One doesn't have to be a general practitioner for long before discovering that a great deal of ill-health and suffering results from stress. It is widely accepted in the medical world that a high proportion of commonly seen conditions are psychosomatic in origin, that is, the direct or indirect result of the way we live. Some years ago the famous Mayo clinic quoted 85% as a possible figure. As we come to understand more we may find it is even higher.

There can't be any of us who have not experienced the effects of stress at some time or another, perhaps many times a day. We would have to shut ourselves away from normal life to avoid it and then the sheer boredom and loneliness would produce its own variety of stress.

It's not surprising that stress should be so prevalent when we remember that everything we think, do or feel involves some physical and chemical change in the cells of our bodies. Even thinking itself is a chemical process. Mostly we are unaware of these complicated reactions going on inside us but if we meet a sudden emergency, for example, we become conscious of something happening.

Take an emergency on the road. We find ourselves holding our breath. Our heart begins to pound and our skin feels prickly as the hairs stand up on end. We feel frightened because we have come to associate these reactions with threatening situations. We will probably have already jammed on the brakes. Then we have to decide whether we should swerve out of the way or not. If we do, will we hit something or run someone over?

All this happens in a fraction of a second. A team of glands dotted around the body responds to a stimulus from a small area of the brain, the hypothalamus, itself triggered off by what the eye has seen or the ear has heard. As a result adrenalin and other potent chemicals pour into the blood stream, finding their way to the appropriate nerves and muscles.

The body usually settles down again quite quickly, though we may be left shaking and sweating for a while. After being blown up by the mine in Singapore harbour it was about three months before I stopped jumping whenever a door banged. If there is severe alarm, it may lead to shock with the blood pressure, which has shot up during the emergency, now falling to perhaps dangerous levels.

A similar process goes on whenever we are faced with something we don't like or which seems to threaten us in some way. Have you ever felt shaky after an argument? My own voice becomes tremulous on these occasions and my eyes fill with tears which can be very embarrassing. At school we used to take girlish delight in watching the redness creep up the neck of our geography mistress when someone annoyed her.

A famous physician, William Hunter, said that his life was in the hands of anyone who could make him angry. He died in a fit of temper.

It is usually stress which has gone on for a long time or keeps recurring which sends people to their doctors. Certain parts of the body seem particularly vulnerable – blood pressure, stomach, bowels, joints and skin are common target areas. Some people react by becoming over-anxious or depressed. Others, feeling the stress of loneliness or neglect, may produce a wide range of symptoms, varying from one consultation to another, for which no organic cause can be found. One patient of ours went so far as to simulate complete paralysis for a few days, while another insisted she had gone blind in one eye. It was only with great difficulty that we could get her to open it.

A little girl came to the surgery with a bigger sister who was definitely ill. She must have felt temporarily abandoned as our attention was focused on her sister. As I was examining the patient, a pathetic little voice starting complaining that she was ill too. "Rubbish," said mother. "There's nothing wrong with you." But the wailing persisted and there were real tears, so when I had finished with the patient I started to ask questions – "Does your nose hurt?" "Yes." Does your big toe hurt?" "Yes." I then proceeded to pummel her from head to toe as she lay solemn-faced on the couch. Gradually a grin began to spread over her face and when I had finished, she jumped down and danced happily out of the room.

Of course it is also possible to get a stiff neck from sitting in a draught, or indigestion from eating too many potato chips.

Far and away the commonest form of stress lies in personal relationships. Here it is often the drip-ping-on-a-stone type of pressure which does the damage. An outwardly placid woman kept coming with an irritating skin rash which disappeared when she had a day off or went away on holiday. She and I finally decided it must be due to the fact that she was the manageress of a works canteen where she had to supervise a number of girls who preferred chatting and giggling to getting on with their work. This irritated her intensely but she was far too controlled to lose her temper. They literally "got under her skin".

For another it was a painful right knee. Before I could say anything she herself made the interesting suggestion that it might be psychological. When I asked her why, she told me that her son's wife had just walked out on him and the children and this had made her very angry. "You mean you would like to kick her," I said. "Yes, I would," she agreed.

A man who had headaches and couldn't sleep said he had no problems at home so I questioned him about his work. Without hesitation he said, "It's the manager's fault. He's always pushing me around. I hate him." With jobs difficult to find he didn't dare leave.

I once visited a newly-married man who complained of abdominal pains which came and went. He seemed extremely anxious. The house was immaculate with a brand new carpet on the floor, the most modern furniture, a colour television, an indoor aquarium and a large dog. He and his wife had both been working full-time to pay for these things and the strain was telling on them. He complained that his wife didn't bother enough about the house and cooking and he had to do more than his share. She complained that he didn't realise how tired she was at the end of a day's work and that he spent too much time looking after the fish and the dog. She was planning to go home to mother.

Stress is simply the result of the way in which we resist the challenges which life inevitably presents us with. There is hardly a moment when we are not faced with a challenge of some sort. How do I react, for example, when the telephone goes just as I have plunged my hands into a bowl of sticky dough, or I am watching a special television programme? It actually went five times as I was writing this page, just to try me out.

The reason why we react in such uncomfortable ways is that we feel threatened. It may be a simple threat to our time or energy but more often it is to something deeper.

When I first went on the wards as a student, I expected to begin learning straight away how to treat the patients, but for several weeks treatment was not even mentioned. The only thing that seemed to matter was getting the diagnosis right. We were made to stand at the foot of a bed, gaze at the patient and guess what was wrong before we even had a chance to lay a finger on him or see the results of laboratory tests. I eventually realised the wisdom of this. Once we knew what was wrong the treatment was simply a matter of applying the most up-to-date tools which science had put into our hands. The real skill lay in accurate diagnosis.

In diagnosing physical complaints, pain and

discomfort are among our most useful indicators. They are simply warnings of something wrong. They start people looking for help and once they do this they are well on the way to cure. The trouble with leprosy is that the sense of pain is destroyed so a patient may injure himself without knowing it. Some people with mental illness are quite unaware that they are ill and this makes it very difficult to help them.

In searching for the reason behind pain, the doctor looks for the site of maximum tenderness. As he prods and probes he will deliberately add to the patient's discomfort, watching the patient's face to see when he winces, as most adults are too controlled to cry out.

At this stage it can be very tempting to offer immediate relief of pain. This, of course, is what the patient would like too. But it would be considered gross malpractice for a doctor to abolish a patient's acute abdominal pain before he had formed an opinion as to its probable cause. This may sometimes mean leaving the patient in pain until some decision can be reached. Failure to observe this basic rule could result in the patient dying for lack of accurate diagnosis.

It is just the same when we are dealing with illness brought about by reaction to the stresses and strains of everyday life. It is equally poor practice to treat only the presenting symptom, though it is usually all the patient expects, and with all the new drugs at our disposal it is only too easy to do. To uncover the real cause of the trouble may take more time than we think we have and may be distressing to the patient and a source of stress to ourselves.

But if doctors are prepared to get involved, we may find an answer which in the long run will save both time and a great deal of money, in addition to the relief which the patient will experience.

A young married woman came yet again for relief of her recurring mouth ulcers. This time I asked her whether she had been through any emotional upsets, and after some hesitation she told me that her real worry was the revulsion she felt towards her first child, now five years old. She felt very guilty about this and had never mentioned it to anyone. She tried hard not to let it show but there were times when she could hardly bear to look at him, let alone cuddle or kiss him.

It turned out that he was the child of a boy-friend who had deserted her for someone else in the middle of her pregnancy. It had been one of those uncommitted relationships which, as often happens, meant much more to the girl than the boy. The child had been happily accepted by her husband but for her he was a constant reminder of her rejection and shame.

Bringing all this out was a painful business and it was some time before she could stop crying. It was not easy for her to face her own part in the situation, or to forgive the man who had hurt her so much, but she realised she must do this. To her amazement she found that from then on she actually began to want to play with and cuddle the small boy and that he started coming to her of his own accord, whereas before he had often shied away from her. They went off for a day alone together at her husband's suggestion to celebrate, and the ulcers cleared.

Within one week I was visited by a husband and wife with identical symptoms, neither of them aware that the other was planning to see a doctor. The wife came first. She complained of indigestion from which she had suffered for some time but which had lately become much worse and more persistent. It looked as though she might have developed an ulcer, but I decided to see if it would settle, before subjecting her to a barium meal. She denied any stress factors in her life.

When her husband turned up complaining of the same symptoms, I began to wonder what was going on. He told me they were eating the usual food and that they had no financial worries, but then he told me that their twenty-year-old son, who lived with them, had recently become increasingly abusive and aggressive towards them. His mother always rushed to his defence but he was just as rude to her. Mealtimes were a misery. "I can't understand it," he said. "We've always given him everything he wanted."

We talked about what could be done. The husband had felt annoyed with his wife and he now decided to make things up with her. He thought they should talk things over and see if they could agree on a common policy on what they expected of their son and how the house should be run, and stand up for this together. I agreed that this was more likely to give their son the security and direction he clearly needed than always giving in to him and disagreeing between themselves. They might even lose their ulcers in the process. One bottle of medicine was all they needed.

"For God's sake, doctor, give me a tranquilliser or I shall go round the bend!" – when the woman I described at the beginning of this chapter had finished pouring out her troubles, I had to decide what to do. As a Christian I was sure that there must be a more permanent answer to her problems than the one she had demanded. But how do you say this to an angry, hurt lady whose manner does little to suggest she ever gives God a thought?

As often happens the answer was easier than I had expected. What she said about a "wall" between her and her husband reminded me that in two days' time I was planning to go with a party to see a play at a theatre which specialised in Christian drama. I thought it might have something to offer her, so tentatively invited her to join me, feeling slightly stupid as I made the unlikely suggestion. To my surprise she agreed. The play turned out to be all about the walls which people build up between themselves and their neighbours, class and class, East and West – whichever way one liked to see it. It vividly and humourously showed the way God, in the guise of a doctor, moved freely from one side to the other with equal concern for both and with scant regard for walls of any kind. My patient was quick to see the point. On the way home she said she recognised that the wall she had imagined between her and her husband was as much of her making as his and that obviously God cared for both of them. There was no more need for a tranquilliser.

Mrs A was a pillar of her church, always going to meetings which she was convinced could not manage without her. In addition she had a senile father-in-law to look after and a husband and son who relied on her to get them up in the morning in time for work. She complained that she could not keep up with all she had to do. She looked harassed and had a perpetual headache and palpitations, so I was not surprised to find that she had a very high blood pressure.

She looked surprised when, after examining her, I suggested she might like to try starting the day a few minutes earlier still by being quiet and asking God to show her what to do, what not to do and how to react to her demanding family. I gave her something to help her get off to sleep.

When she returned a fortnight later, her hair was tidy and her blood pressure was normal. She said she had done as I suggested and was now coping happily. The work was the same and she still went to her meetings but no longer felt any pressure to do so. She now found she managed everything with time to spare to help her busy neighbour with her washing.

Not all cases of raised blood pressure are due to stress but a great many are. Since trying this prescription out on Mrs A, I have offered it to other patients with equally good results.

Stress is a polite word and we feel no shame in admitting that we suffer from it. In fact we can often put the blame on someone else. But like any other illness it is helpful to give it its real name if we are to get the treatment right. Just as hypertension, peptic ulcer, asthma or arthritis may be the physical outcome, so resentment, clinging to our rights, fear, jealousy or hurt pride may be the underlying cause. Likewise indifference, criticism or demand in us may be the cause of someone else's ill-health.

One day I had a particularly bad attack of house-wife's stress. Everyone seemed to be demanding something of me at the same time. I was trying to get on with my own work when one of our sons demanded that I should find some missing article for him immediately; my husband wanted something done, that moment and no later; a patient staying in the house was hanging around wanting to talk; and the telephone started to ring and no one else answered it. Resentment flooded over me and with my head spinning I abandoned the lot, including the telephone, and dashed upstairs out of the way. "How much am I supposed to take?" I shouted inwardly. "You can take just as much as I care to give you," God seemed to reply. My resentment collapsed and I found myself laughing. I returned to the fray feeling relaxed and ready for anything. No one seemed a nuisance any more. It was a matter of saying "Yes" instead of "No".

3

Why Should It Happen To Me?

Even when we have eliminated the ill health caused
by stress, we are still left with much suffering which
is inexplicable or seems undeserved. Some people go
through a great deal more of it than others. Our
training as doctors helps us to diagnose the trouble
and to weigh up the advantages and disadvantages
of various kinds of treatment. We go on learning all
the time, in fact it is a constant race to keep up to
date. One consultant told me he never read anything
but medical literature even on holiday. Yet none of
this makes it any easier when we come up against
the emotional suffering which goes with illness and
bereavement. What do you say, for example, to a
young mother whose perfectly normal week-old baby
has been found dead in its cot, or to the parents of
a bouncing nine-year-old on whose arm you have
just found a swelling which you know must be
cancer? Nor does our training answer the questions
which we are all tempted to ask when suffering hits
us, "Why should it happen to me?" or "Why does
God allow it?"

Perhaps suffering is easier to accept when we

realise that we are, after all, part of a physical universe. We share the world with millions of other living organisms and there is a constant struggle to keep the balance between us. Too many streptococci in the throat of a child will result in an attack of tonsilitis. In the ensuing battle, with antibiotics on the side of the child, most of the streptococci will die, their bodies swallowed up by the child's own white blood cells. We don't waste time feeling sorry for them. On the other hand, many micro-organisms live in or on our bodies and we are dependent on them to keep us healthy.

I never cease to wonder at the normal healthy growth and renewal of tissues which goes on unnoticed all the time. Just think of the sheer toughness of a new-born baby launched precipitately into a strange environment. How is it that a finger grows to a certain length, and then stops, or that from one minute microscopic cell come all the widely differing organs of the body? There are so many things which can go wrong that the marvel is that it doesn't happen more often.

People react very differently to suffering. In our practice we had two patients who suffered from Menière's disease, which affects the inner ear causing deafness, giddiness and noises in the head. One patient described her noises as "all the devils in hell". The other, who was completely deaf and bedridden, said hers sounded like "choirs of angels".

We have had many people suffering from depression in our home. One would demand attention all the time and cast gloom over the whole household, while another, just as ill, somehow kept her feelings to herself and even managed to smile.

There is little I can add to all that has been written on the problem of suffering. All I have learned from people who have suffered is that it need never be a totally negative experience, and that it can add a richness to life which is unique. A new quality seems to come into the most ordinary person.

I once went to visit a friend who had had a stroke. She had been an outstanding craftswoman and well-known for her soft toy making. Here she was, totally unable to do anything for herself, yet all her talk was about the kindness of people and the book she was going to write about the funny things which went on around her.

Another friend slipped on a patch of polish when he was eighteen and was completely paralysed as a result of a brain haemorrhage. Although he speaks with difficulty and can barely move his hands, he is always the first to see a joke and we get occasional typed letters of a few lines from him which may have taken several hours to produce. They sound as if his life is full. There is no hint of self-pity.

For some an operation may be the high point of their lives when, perhaps for the first time, they have been the centre of attention, fussed over and cared for. A few years ago one would often hear women talking dramatically about the time when they "had everything taken away". This always left me with visions of vast empty spaces, puzzled as to how they managed to function at all. A better knowledge of anatomy seems to have reduced this operation to its right proportions.

Strangely it is often the minor complaints which are hardest to put up with. Talk of aching joints or the exquisite pain of corns often arouses more annoyance than sympathy or attention. So people suffer, feeling that no one understands or is as bad as they are – and sometimes getting quite competitive in the process.

I found it extremely irritating when an elderly friend who was also a patient spent twenty minutes or so every time we met socially, telling me about her latest pain, often when there were other people in the room I wanted to talk to. One day I felt I should stop merely being irritated and, for her sake as much as for mine, do something about it.

She was most apologetic when I broached the subject and she realised how self-centred she had become. To help herself get over this, she decided to have a daily newspaper in front of her during that time in the morning when she read her Bible and to pray for the people mentioned in the headlines. She became so interested in this that she had to have a map of the world spread out on her bed as well. She still had her aches and pains and we would discuss these at the appropriate times, but she now had other things to talk about as well and felt involved in world affairs.

At the other extreme are those who don't talk enough about their problems. I am amazed how long some people keep suffering to themselves, whether it is stress-induced or not. Physical and mental suffering can become so much worse if we try to cope with it on our own, and relief can come simply from sharing it with someone we trust.

A seven-year-old girl, pale and shivery with a basin beside her in case of emergency, said, "I feel much better when I am talking to someone." As we talked her cheeks turned pink and the basin was forgotten.

In our practice we have often witnessed the easing of severe pain once it has been talked about and explained. My husband once visited a young man lying in bed because his pain was too bad for him to move around. His first question was, "Have I got cancer?" Ken knew he had, but had been forbidden by the family to tell him, so he asked, "What do you think?" "Well," answered the young man, "I think I must have because I'm obviously not getting any better and all they are giving me are painkillers."

Our experience has been that honesty, difficult though it may be, is always best on these occasions and that if we are ready the right moment for the truth will present itself. Without honesty, a barrier of doubt and distrust can build up between the patient and his doctor and, more important, between the patient and his family at a time when they most need each other's support. There is also a great richness to be had from going through these experiences together.

The next question the young man asked was whether his condition was catching. He had been afraid to kiss his wife and small girl in case he should pass on anything to them. Meanwhile his wife had been distressed by his apparent aloofness. With the relief which the truth brought him, he began to get up and live normally with the family and with very little pain. He died quite suddenly one day during a family tea-party.

Death is perhaps the most important moment of our lives. It is certainly as normal a part as being born. It should be the climax. A Scottish lady in her nineties, who had no family of her own and spent her last two years in our home, used to say, "When you get to my age, you can't help wondering just what's round the corner. If what the Bible says is true, it will be wonderful." She slipped away one day with one of our boys doing his homework in her room and the dog curled up peacefully on the floor by her bed.

It is good to know that God can have death in his hands as well as life. My brother-in-law was well aware that he had cancer but thought he still had several months to live. His family were scattered round the world and we did not even know just where his daughter was at that moment. One morning we felt strongly that God was telling us to get the family home. We phoned his son in Australia to find that he and his wife, who were due home in a few weeks' time, had already packed their things, and so were ready to take off. The daughter we discovered had arrived at her brother's house in Canada the day before. All of them were home within a few days and a week later their father died. He had written in his notebook a day or two before,

"Whatever the Lord does, He is always to be trusted – always."

Suffering has its own healing quality as well. A patient, who became a close friend of mine, had felt separated from her daughter-in-law and longed to see this put right. Then she was found to have cancer. As soon as she was no longer able to be left alone, her daughter-in-law offered to come and look after her. This seemed like a miracle in itself. It meant heavy and often unpleasant nursing but her daughter-in-law did this cheerfully. As the days went by the two of them became very close and appreciative of each other.

One day near the end, I was with them. I had been surprised how little had been needed in the way of pain relief, but it was still very distressing at times to watch her apparent suffering. I say "apparent" because after one bad bout she relaxed on her pillow and said, "You know, the peace of God really does pass all understanding," and there was no doubt in either of our minds that she meant it. When it was all over the daughter-in-law told me she wouldn't have missed the experience for anything.

In some ways mental illness causes the most difficult suffering of all because it affects the way we think and feel. It is impossible for anyone in the depths of a depression to "pull up his socks" as his friends will almost certainly advise him to do.

Some depression is, of course, caused simply by things going wrong in a person's life. It may be bereavement, loss of a job or separation from the family. This will pass either with time or as the patient accepts a new attitude to life, which in itself may require acceptance or forgiveness.

There is much depressive illness, however, for which no definite reason is clear. In these cases there appears to be a chemical malfunctioning in the brain which produces a sensation of depression. Not understanding why this should be, patients often search around for a reason. They may blame others or more commonly have a strong sense of personal guilt. Sometimes it is this, and sometimes it is the fact that physical symptoms predominate, which makes it difficult to convince a patient that there is an under-lying depressive illness needing treatment. Fortu-nately these days we have drugs to offer which can suppress or reverse the chemical reactions and promise most patients light at the end of the tunnel.

A woman I know suddenly felt one morning as though she had committed a crime, though no unusual misdoing occurred to her. Finally she stopped struggling with her housework and asked God where she had gone wrong. The answer came clearly, "Don't worry, this is purely physical." She still felt under a cloud but the sense of guilt had gone and a few hours later she realised that it was the time of the month which usually passed her by without causing trouble, but when many women are vulner-able to depression. Sure enough the depression lifted within a few hours.

A notoriously difficult mental illness to treat is one in which the patient is gripped by an obsession of some kind. A young married woman was obsessed by the fear that she might "contaminate" her family. She was afraid to handle food or to do the washing. She was afraid to leave the house in case she touched anything unclean which might bring harm to them. Everything, whether clothes or food utensils, had to be washed several times over and even then she was not satisfied that it was clean enough. She was a gifted girl and longed to do something useful with her life, so felt very frustrated by her fears.

It seemed that one possible explanation lay in the fact that as a child she had once hit her brother over the head with a golf club and had been told that she might have killed him. This did not affect her too deeply until she had a family of her own. However, suggesting a possible reason was not enough in itself to release her.

As she was a Christian, we were able to pray together and she gradually learned the kind of prayer which includes expecting God to speak as well as listen to us. One day she was trying to decide whether a towel was clean enough to use or whether she needed to wash it yet again. As she stood there, the thought came into her mind, "It's all right, go ahead and use it." This thought came with such authority that she felt she could trust it, so she used the towel. From that time things became easier and she is now living a full life in her community with people constantly in and out of her home.

We hear much these days about the "innocent victims" of violence and we watch appalled as the TV shows us pictures of the latest bomb outrage. Many things happen to people which are the fault of someone else. The added tragedy of these events lies in the contagious infection of bitterness which they leave behind. This is when we hear "Why does God allow it?" shouted most loudly.

I once met a woman who had been badly crippled in an accident caused by a drunken driver. To begin with, as she lay in hospital, she was angry and resentful. She found herself again and again asking "Why?". One day, instead of "Why?" she began to ask herself "What for?". Immediately she started to think of all she had learned and could learn from the experience, and how her whole life would have a different value because of it. She took an interest in the patient in the next bed and found she could help her through her difficulties. When she left hospital, she found that because she was no longer able to dash around being busy, she had more time for people who visited her. By the time I met her, although she could only walk with the help of two sticks and was constantly in pain, she had an infectious gaiety which anyone might envy.

Another "innocent victim" was brought to me by her mother at her school's request. The day before, she had been badly beaten up by a gang of girls. She had bruises on her face, arms and legs. There seemed no reason for the attack.

She was bright, well-dressed and quite clearly came from a family where she was loved. Apparently she was good at games and popular with her classmates. As we talked I remembered a bully at our daughter's primary school who came from a broken home. We had decided to pray for her, hoping this might help our daughter to be less afraid of her. Our daughter and her friends had deliberately thought out ways of making friends with her. In the end she had been elected the first honorary member of a newly-formed "Friendly Society" in the school and the bullying stopped.

I told the girl and her mother this story. They said that the girl's attackers did not do very well at school and all had parents who were either separated or rarely at home. Maybe they were jealous, I suggested. Perhaps praying for them might help, just as it had in our daughter's case.

A few months later I saw the girl again about another matter and asked what had happened. She looked at her mother and they both laughed. "We did pray," she said, "and two days later the leader of the gang came and apologised and said she didn't know what had come over them." A few weeks later at Easter, they had given her a present.

I saw the mother about a year after the incident and she told me how surprised the headmaster was at the friendship which had sprung up between her daughter and the gang-leader.

One couple I know thought very seriously about whether God wanted them to have a second child. When they had made up their minds, the wife came to me for a check-up. There seemed no reason why they should not go ahead. When the baby arrived he was a mongol. At first they were shaken and puzzled but when I met the mother a year later she told me how grateful they were for the experience and how much they loved the little boy. Instead of breaking their faith it had in fact added to it. "We have learned that being Christians doesn't exempt us from suffering but that God is with us in it," she said.

4

Home Help!

There is an old joke which asks, "Why can't we all live together like one big family?" and answers, "The trouble is – we do."

A certain amount of quarrelling and bickering is accepted as part of family life. Yet a man told me that the reason why things went so well in the small factory where he worked was that it was "just like a family". He meant, of course, that it was small and intimate enough for everyone to know everyone else.

We all dream of "Home Sweet Home", the place where all is peace, where we belong and are recognised as equals. During the nights in the internment camp, I would frequently dream of home, of falling into my mother's arms, eating Sunday dinners of roast lamb or sitting by the fire. When we came back after the war and I found myself getting irritated with my mother when I heard her correcting our small daughter, it was as though I was trampling on my own dreams. But the fact that the reality is so often different from the ideal does not stop us wanting it or expecting it. Everybody, in spite of the problems they experience, wants to be part of a happy family. The question is, how?

Because we haven't found the answer to that question, divorce has become commonplace. One in three marriages in Britain now end that way, but most divorced people get married again, hoping for better things next time. It reflects a longing for something different and more lasting.

Many people who do not normally go to church like to have a church wedding. They feel it adds beauty, dignity, and, perhaps, hope to the occasion. I asked an American who was about to embark on her third church wedding, what she did about marriage vows. "Oh," she said, "we might promise to stay together as long as love lasts." One is tempted to ask why promise anything? Some grit their teeth and stay together for the sake of the children, others opt for living together without any legal commitment. "I don't want to go through the hell my parents went through," one girl told me.

"What! Stay with one man all your life? How boring!" a lively nineteen-year-old gasped when I suggested that lasting marriage might be feasible. So how important is it that a man and a woman should make a supreme effort to stay together "for better, for worse"?

If the experience of GPs up and down the country is anything to go by, secure marriages are very important, if only for the sake of people's health. One of the most time-consuming parts of a doctor's work these days is trying to steer patients through the traumas of a broken or breaking marriage with minimum damage to their health. On average a doctor sees twelve to twenty patients during a surgery. One of these is likely to be ill because of friction in the home and this one may take more time than three or four others put together. Often there is more than one, and what we see is probably only the tip of an iceberg. It may be the woman who lives in constant fear that her husband will go off with someone else or the one whose husband does leave her for the woman across the road. There must be many marriages held in a fragile balance by the liberal use of tranquillisers. The skill required to deal with these situations is not yet taught in medical schools.

Then there are the children. A magistrate friend of mine says that most juvenile offenders she deals with come from broken homes. Not all go so far as to break the law but some leave home rather than put up with the parental friction.

My own family was a happy one most of the time, though one of my sisters was a notorious biter in her youth, while I reduced my younger sister to a quivering jelly in my attempts to cure her of her fear of the dark. I never told her how frightened I was of it myself. At least we all took it for granted that we were loved and wanted and that we would always come home to the same welcome from the same parents.

Our parents reserved their most heated debates for the time when we were supposed to be asleep. Although it never entered my head that they would ever separate, the sound of their voices rising from the floor below conjured up in my mind a terrifying picture of wandering alone and lost in a dark wet street in a large unknown city.

One night, after a day in which my husband and I had had an argument, our daughter, who had seen several of her friends' parents break up, asked with real anxiety, "You would never divorce Daddy, would you?" What goes on in the minds of children whose parents do break up?

I think of a girl at an élite boarding school, who did not know at the end of the term which home she was supposed to go to for the holidays. Her parents were in such a tangle of divorces and remarriages, that they forgot to tell her. She ended up by being cared for by the butler. Such situations hardly bear thinking about.

A girl of twelve was brought to me because the school had been complaining about her frequent absences. Mother said it was because she always felt sick in the mornings and was quite unfit to go to school. She usually recovered as the day went on. It is not uncommon for children to have tummy-aches or to feel sick when it is time to go to school, but this seemed excessive for a girl of her age.

Conversation revealed that her father had walked out of the home one morning when she was four. I asked her whether she remembered the day this happened. Without hesitation she said, "Yes, I do. It was raining, I was crying and the washing machine was going."

She had kept in touch with her father but now, involved in his new domestic affairs and with another family coming on, he seemed to be losing interest and she felt he did not love her any more. As we talked she realised that, without consciously thinking about it, she had become afraid that she would come home from school one day to find her mother gone too.

Rejection is just about the greatest ill that can befall a human being, especially feeling pushed on one side in favour of someone else.

One day a woman was given a new car by her husband. The next day he went off to work as usual but in the evening he phoned her to say he had found someone he would rather live with and that was that. Up to that time he had been the centre and whole purpose of her life. She had no other interests. It took two years before she was well enough to go back to work. She contemplated suicide several times. Only the discovery that God still loved her, whatever else happened, saved her and put her back on her feet.

It isn't only couples who can be afraid of losing each other, or children of losing their parents. Parents can be just as afraid of losing their children. Adolescents can so easily walk out of the home. One girl left home after a row with her father and it was eight years before they even knew where she was. The psychiatrist, Doris Odlum, writing on this subject, says that it is important never to slam the door shut. But fear can make for sudden outbursts of temper which can close doors for ever. Fear can also blackmail parents into giving in to their children or compromising over things which they feel to be wrong.

Fear had a strangely paralysing effect on me. Our fifteen-year-old son would bring his friends into the house through the kitchen without a word and into the sitting-room, shutting the door firmly behind him. I would be left wondering what on earth they were talking about and what dastardly schemes they were hatching. I did not dare to interrupt them or ask what they were up to. It was an absurd situation and my behaviour became more and more unnatural.

Before the next school holidays started I felt things had got to be different so I asked God what to do about it. The uncomplicated answer which sprang to my mind was, "Be his Mum." I immediately remembered him as a small boy, kicking and punching as I carried him away from the dinner table, where he had been creating havoc, and into the small bathroom under the stairs where I held him firmly till the violence subsided, a thumb slipped into his mouth and, with a suck and a sigh, he surrendered to my embrace.

As I thought of this my fear fell away. From then on I was able to talk naturally and to enter into what he and his friends were doing, although I am well aware that there were many things I never did know about. They seemed to take me for granted, and if there was any generation gap, it had been of my own making.

Children do not have to reach their teens before parents can be afraid of losing them. One young mother came to me in a state of great distress. That day her five-year-old son had told her that he didn't like her any more and wished she'd go away. She felt a complete failure as a mother and asked me whether I thought she should leave home or hand the boy over to the care of the local authority.

Fortunately I had experienced this sort of thing myself. Our children were never the sort to pull their punches. "I sometimes wish there weren't such things as parents," one of our loving children once said gloomily when we stopped him doing something he wanted to do. On occasions I had felt that about my own parents whom I loved very much, so I was not unduly shocked. It pays to look back and remember what we were like as children, for ours are very much the same underneath.

A conference on the family which I attended came to the conclusion that a major reason for breakdown was lack of communication. This was certainly true of one seventeen-year-old who came to see me because she was over three months pregnant. She had been too scared to tell anyone earlier. As soon as she had realised she was pregnant, she had slipped out of the house without her parents knowing and had been living in a poky little room in a friend's house. She had been convinced that if her parents discovered they would throw her out anyway. Now she was frightened and alone, but the thought of telling her parents frightened her still more.

Finally I persuaded her to let me go and see them. When, with some trepidation, I told them what had happened, they both broke down. "Why couldn't she have told us she was in trouble?" asked the father. "Surely she must have known that we loved her and would do anything to help her." But for some reason she just hadn't.

Another girl told me how she had burst into the sitting-room of her home one day to tell her mother she had just got engaged. Before she could say anything, her mother patted the seat next to her, kept her eyes glued to the television and said, "Go and get yourself a drink, then come and sit down and be quiet." The girl told me later that she still hadn't got around to telling her about the engagement.

Germaine Greer, one of the pioneers of women's liberation, described the family of the sixties as "self-contained, self-centred and short-lived". She therefore rejected it. Maybe it is not the family we should be rejecting but the self-centredness.

Unhappy-looking women, and occasionally men, come to the surgery suffering from the stresses of a struggling marriage and cry, "But I must think of myself." My heart aches for them because I know that if they could stop doing just that, life would take on a completely different colour. Staying the way they are is only making things more difficult and adding to the hopelessness of the situation.

One day when Ken and I were working together in general practice, Mrs M came complaining of a severe headache. Ken sensed that there was more to this headache than met the eye. He asked her to come back later with her husband so that the four of us could spend time together. Her husband, who was a Jewish hairdresser, suffered from asthma. He was also very fond of his food. As soon as they sat down, the mud-slinging started. There had been an increasing number of rows between them lately, and the climax had come that day when he arrived home for his dinner. Although Mrs M had remembered to put the meat in the oven, she had forgotten to light the gas. What might have been a joke was the last straw. He had flung the uncooked meat across the room at her and had threatened to leave.

At last Ken called a halt. He said he wanted to be quiet for a few moments to think over what they had been saying and suggested they might like to do likewise. Up to this point there had been no mention of God and we had no idea how they felt about Him. After a few minutes Mr M broke the silence. "I know what you're getting at, Doc," he said. "I originally trained as a Rabbi but there was no money in it so I gave it up. I would like to start again if Elsa is willing." "I used to be a Methodist," said Mrs M, "but when I got married I dropped it all." Then she told us of how, many years before, she had gone to help a member of her family who was living in what was then Persia and was in great trouble. She had had no idea what to do and felt in despair about it all.

While she was sitting in Beirut airport waiting for her flight, a young Arab student came over and asked if he could do anything to help. He had noticed how worried she looked. She found herself pouring out all her anxieties to him. He told her that if she would listen to God's voice inside her heart, He would tell her what to do. She tried this, found it worked and the family problem was solved. She had kept up the habit of listening to God for a while but the business of life had pushed it out. Now after all these years, she found herself being asked to do it once more, and she knew it was something she must never let go of again.

Their marriage not only stuck but blossomed over the next thirty years up to his death a short time ago.

The best recipe for a stick-together family is "Change starts with me". Jesus said, "Why do you notice the speck in your brother's eye and fail to notice the plank in your own?" Whenever I have felt hard done by and have referred the matter to God, He has never failed to point out some way in which I was wrong, and this of course gives me quite a different view of the situation.

Children are a great help in discovering this. Once in a moment of exasperation I hit my small daughter in the middle of her back and winded her. The blow had been intended for lower down but a sudden squirm on her part meant it misfired. As she gasped for breath, I held her on my lap and said I was sorry. "Sometimes," I said, "you are horrid and I have to help you not to be, and sometimes I am horrid and you must help me." "Yes," she sobbed, "that's what you've got a little girl for."

A mother told me how, in the silence which followed a heated argument between her and her husband, their small girl had said, "Now go on – love him."

One evening after a stormy scene, one of our boys had been sent to bed early. Later on, when I had simmered down and was feeling bad about my lost temper, I went up to his room. He was curled up underneath the bedclothes. I knelt down by the bed and after a few moments, an arm appeared and wrapped itself round my neck.

Anyone who has experienced forgiveness given and received, knows how worthwhile the struggle is.

But apology may come too late. The saddest case I ever had to deal with was that of an elderly man whose wife had died in the middle of breakfast. There she was, slumped over the table, a half-eaten boiled egg in front of her, the spoon still in her hand. The old man was deeply distressed, not so much, as he said, because she had died – he had expected that to happen before long – but because they had been having an argument when it happened. "And it wasn't even over anything important," he said. "If only you could bring her back long enough for me to say I'm sorry."

Starting the car to go home one evening, the thought came into my mind that I should visit a family I had not seen for some time. I resisted the idea firstly because I was tired and secondly because the family had not asked for a visit and it might be difficult to explain why I had gone. It could be just one of those bright ideas which led nowhere. I therefore took the common sense way and turned the car homewards. But the thought quietly persisted. Reluctantly I did a U-turn and headed for the family's home. I had heard it said that it is better to make a mistake than to make nothing.

When I knocked on the door, it was opened by
the wife who, without a word of welcome or even
surprise, withdrew hastily into the kitchen on the
left. Father then appeared briefly in the doorway
of the sitting-room on the right. The eight-year-old
daughter sat with her chin on her hands, halfway up
the staircase in the middle, and looked at me with
large unhappy eyes.

I closed the door behind me and stepping into
the small hall, waited for someone to say something.
At last mother said, "We've come to the end of the
road. Either he goes or I go." I stood silently praying
for some illuminating thought, but as none came, I
said, "Well, I don't know what the answer is, but I
do know that God minds what happens to you all,
because He told me to come. I am sure He can tell
you what to do." There was no comment from either
room so, after a few more moments of complete
silence, I let myself out of the house and went home.

I heard nothing more, but a few weeks later I
happened to catch a glimpse of them in a crowded
place. They all waved cheerfully and it was clear to
me that all was well. I met the daughter recently and
she confirmed that the family was still together and
happy.

A woman faced with difficult problems in her
family once told me she wondered whether there
was any point in struggling to find the answer.
Wouldn't it be more sensible just to give up and get
out? I have found that the lessons I have learned at
home have often proved more useful to patients than
the prescriptions I have given them. So I encouraged

her to keep going. For if she could find a way of putting things right in her own home, she would have discovered something far more valuable than even her own or her family's happiness. She would have a valid recipe to offer anyone in difficulties in any situation.

Home does not have to be a place of luxury with all modern conveniences for it to succeed. As we looked, half-starved, out of our filthy, broken warehouse windows on a bitter winter day in 1944, we saw a group of Chinese children in their padded clothes, hugging themselves against the cold. "Look at those poor little kids," said our three-year-old, "they haven't got a lovely home like we have."

5

Nothing To Do With The Law

"I want a closer relationship with my boy-friend so I must have the Pill." The blue-eyed fifteen-year-old fixed me with a look which challenged me to dare to refuse. She had brought two friends with her as a bodyguard. I accepted the challenge. "It's against the law to have intercourse under sixteen," I said as blandly as I could. "The law has nothing whatever to do with it," was her response. "I want it." So much for the law. "I am not willing to give it to you," I said. "In that case you will have an abortion on your hands," she replied. "That," I said, "is your responsibility." A fierce battle ensued and she left without the Pill, saying she would find a doctor who would "co-operate".

I didn't feel particularly proud of my performance, I would rather have won her confidence. However one of her friends stayed behind to consult me on some minor complaint. "I used to be like her," she said, nodding towards the door, "but my boy-friend and I started going to church. Now we don't want to have sex till we're married, so I don't need the Pill any more." She said this as though she had

53

discovered the answer to an unwelcome problem. Apparently her boy-friend was equally contented with the arrangement.

A chapter on the subject of sex education would have been unthinkable in any decent book when I was growing up. All the sex education I can remember came in a veiled warning about men given me by my mother just as I was leaving home to join the dangerous ranks of medical students. Parents didn't find it any easier then than they do today to talk intelligently about these things with their children. Being one of four girls was an added disadvantage. But thanks to friends at my first school, and to my mother's battered copy of Black's Medical Dictionary, I knew more than my mother realised.

It is a good thing that everything is now much more out in the open and that our attitudes are less inhibited, but is sex really the best "sweetie" life can offer as so many would have us believe? The promoters of sex from the earliest possible age have been so successful that one mother was sure there must be something wrong with her fourteen-year-old daughter because she didn't have a regular boy-friend and didn't seem interested in having one.

For us humans with our highly developed powers of reason and choice and our complex emotions, sex has ceased to be simply the powerful, periodically induced instinct which drives other animals to mate at specified intervals. Along with eating and drinking we have turned sex into a game – a highly profitable one too for those who would exploit it. The last thing many people seem to connect sex with is having children. "I never thought it could happen," said one girl who had been caught unprepared. Some wise virgins on the other hand have come for the Pill for no other reason than that it happens to be their sixteenth birthday.

Too much sexual activity at an early age can be dangerous. There is a higher incidence of cancer later on in those who have had too much too soon or with several different partners. There is the risk of venereal diseases, certain of which can kill the patient or blind a baby. A consultant who specialises in these diseases told me he was "horrified at the deluge of them in recent years, particularly among thirteen and fourteen-year-olds". Apart from the dangerous ones, there are other troublesome infections associated with frequent intercourse which can be very disturbing.

All the contraceptives devised so far are either unpleasant, risky or uncertain. The only method approved by the Roman Catholic Church requires too much self-control for many people. With the advent of the Pill doctors found themselves for the first time in their careers being expected to prescribe potentially dangerous drugs to healthy women. We have got used to doing this now but the fact remains that the Pill is a deliberate interference with the natural functioning of the body.

The most obvious risk of uncontrolled sex, of course, is that of pregnancy itself with the alternative dangers of abortion.

The age of consent was introduced presumably to protect young women from these unnecessary risks. In Britain, it now stands at sixteen – "a danger-ously low age", according to one gynaecologist.

If one is old enough to have intercourse, then society must regard one as old enough to carry all that goes with it, including the emotional demands and the possibility of producing a family. From conversations I have had with sixteen-year-olds and remembering myself at that age, I would say very few are. I can't help feeling that we were the lucky ones, free to enjoy ourselves without having to take sex and all its complications into consideration all the time, and with the prospect of that added relation-ship to look forward to when we got married.

I asked one girl, who had been with a number of men before finally settling on the one she wanted to marry, whether she had any regrets. "Well," she said, "it did spoil things a bit."

"It's such a relief to be treated as a person rather than a toy to be played with," another girl told me after meeting up with a group in her college for whom sex was not a priority.

When a girl asks for the Pill or any other form of contraception, I put her in the picture about the various risks she is running by embarking on this way of life. I then try to give her some idea of the place I feel sex is meant to have within the context of marriage and family life. In view of present day attitudes this can be quite a daunting process. On one occasion the face opposite to me was so devoid of expression that I felt I could have been talking in a foreign language. I told her how difficult I was finding it to explain what I thought. "Oh, please go on, doctor," she said, "you're doing very well."

Some just seem to need reassurance that their own attitudes are not abnormal. A good-looking girl came on behalf of herself and her boy-friend to ask for contraceptive advice. She was seventeen but had no intention of marrying in the foreseeable future. "We might feel differently about each other in a few years' time," she explained.

As I talked to her she became argumentative and told me my ideas were out of date. I responded by suggesting that it was she who was as old-fashioned as the Roman Empire and Adam and Eve, and that what was needed was people who would be brave enough to pioneer a new fashion in living. She continued to knock down every point I raised but suddenly after half an hour of this, she relaxed in her chair and said, "Well, actually, neither I nor my boy-friend really feel it's right."

A sixteen-year-old, whose mother I knew, came to the surgery and was clearly put out to find me on duty. She finally got round to telling me that she wanted the Pill. I launched into my usual explanation of what was involved and urged her to wait and think about it more. She insisted that she must have the Pill "to be safe". "What does your mother think about it?" I asked. In a horrified voice she said her mother knew nothing about it. She wouldn't dare tell her because she would then tell her father and he would kick her out. As it was she had to see her boy-friend in secret. She almost forced me to swear that I would not give her away, something which of

course I would not have done. The best I could do,
as I reluctantly gave her the prescription, was to
urge her to have a talk with her mother as soon as
possible.

She can't have been as convinced as she appeared
to be. She left the packet of pills in such an obvious
place that even if her mother had not suspected
anything, she could hardly have failed to find them.
The next thing I knew was a furious mother on the
phone in the middle of a surgery demanding to know
what right I had to give her daughter the Pill without
consulting her. All I could do was to suggest that she
and her daughter should come and see me together.
Then I waited apprehensively for them to do so.

I need not have been anxious. By the time they
arrived they had already talked it all out between
them. The mother told me she had been fearful and
therefore over-protective of her daughter. She would
not allow her to stay out late at night nor bring boys
to the house. She felt she had been wrong about this.
The girl had been torn between her mother and her
friends. She didn't really want to have intercourse
yet, but without her mother's support and advice,
which she dared not ask for, she did not know how
to cope with what she imagined was expected of her.
All the fury had evaporated and the fear vanished.

If, in spite of what I say, a girl over sixteen still
insists on having the Pill then, as it is her legal right,
I give her the prescription plus the responsibility to
choose whether to use it or not.

A recent court judgment exonerating a GP who
prescribed the Pill for a fifteen-year-old without the

consent of her parents has made it harder for doctors to uphold the law, where the girl is under age. The General Medical Council has also issued guidelines to doctors telling them not to consult the parents or guardians unless the girl agrees. This seems to me to strike a serious blow to the stability and unity of the family. There must be very few parents who are so unfit to take responsibility for their children that they should not be encouraged and helped to do so. The damage caused by secrecy and such a denial of parents' rights and responsibilities is likely to last a great deal longer than the temporary shock of honesty.

The only justification I can see for prescribing contraception for an under-age girl would be if she was mentally retarded and unable to resist exploitation. This I would regard as treatment rather than social expediency and in such cases the parents or guardians would be fully involved.

I never quite know how to greet a woman whose pregnancy test has proved positive. She will either be delighted or dismayed. Studying her face as she comes through the door may give some indication. If not, I announce the result in a neutral voice and wait anxiously for her reaction. If she is pleased I want to shout with delight and relief. Patients must wonder at my sudden change of expression.

Only too often, unhappily, the response is a desperate "I don't want it". Some simply demand termination as though there was nothing to it.

Agreeing to an abortion was the biggest U-turn the British medical profession ever had to take.

Before the Act of 1967 if a doctor took any part in an abortion, he was struck off the Medical Register and forbidden to practise. As soon as the law was passed, he found himself regarded as callous and inhuman if he so much as questioned it. Doctors who prefer not to take part in performing abortions may find it hard to get jobs in some hospitals.

Many people think that abortion may now be had on demand. In fact the Act states that termination will not be an offence if two registered practitioners are of the "opinion formed in good faith" that to continue the pregnancy would involve more risk to the physical or mental health of the woman or any existing children than would an abortion. In making their decision doctors may take into account the woman's "actual or foreseeable environment".

With the great improvement in ante-natal care, the physical risks to mother and child are now minimal in the western world. There are very few today who need to face abortion on those grounds. As far as the mental health of the woman goes, it is only too easy to take the short-term view. Anti-abortionists criticise doctors for recommending abortion so readily. But it is no easy matter to advise in a cool, detached manner when faced by a distraught woman and an irate husband or mother, even though one feels sure that, given time, the family is more than likely to calm down and accept the situation. Though we are warned of the dangers of refusing to sanction abortion, it is almost unknown for a pregnant woman to commit suicide.

People excuse abortion on the grounds that the

foetus is too small and incomplete to count as a human being. But how big does someone have to be before they matter? Is a six-foot man more important than a four-foot one? Is a sixteen-year-old, whose femurs still have cartilage where there will eventually be bone, less to be considered than an adult whose bones are complete?

The law also permits abortion if there is "substantial risk" that a child would be seriously handicapped physically or mentally. Within the human race there is an enormous variation in physical and mental ability. Who is to decide at what point an individual becomes undesirable?

For doctors who consider a foetus to be a miniature human being with all its human potential, there are two patients to be considered. The danger of abortion to the smaller one is obvious. The risks to the larger one are also considerable. An abortion, especially if performed on a teenage patient, can make future pregnancies more difficult and miscarriages more likely. It is itself a surgical operation with all the accompanying hazards.

Then there are the psychological dangers. Most women I have talked to say they cannot forget that they have had a miscarriage or an abortion. It is a memory a woman has to keep to herself because other people tend to dismiss it as something trivial. Patients often say they keep on wondering what the baby would have been like. Some try hard not to think at all. I asked one if she had thought of her aborted foetus as a person. Her reply was, "No, thank God! If I had I could never have gone through with it." Others have thought again when asked if they mean they would like to have their baby taken away. "I've never thought of it like that," said one.

A girl, who said she had felt great relief immediately after her abortion, came to see me months later with a sudden bout of depression. When we looked at the date of her termination we realised that her depression began on the day on which her baby should have been born. She had never been given this date nor had she consciously worked it out.

Another older woman had recurring depression at the same time each year.

My husband has seen a large number of cases of anorexia nervosa in which the precipitating factor appears to have been an abortion in the family. The patient has recovered when the lost baby has been taken seriously, given a name, and perhaps had a special service held for it in a church.

In the days when the law still prohibited abortion, we had a patient who became pregnant in her late thirties. Her eldest daughter was pregnant at the same time. She was very upset and begged us to do something about it which, of course, we couldn't. All we could do was to see her frequently and give her encouragement through the first few weeks. As we expected she was fine by the time she had reached five months and eventually a baby girl arrived, greeted with delight by all the family.

When the child was ten her father died suddenly. By this time the other children had left home and she became her mother's main support. "I don't know what I would have done without her," said her mother.

"We couldn't possibly cope with a baby," they said as they sat down. The husband was an anxious type and the thought of being a father had completely thrown him. He was out of work so there was little money coming into the home. I felt that a child might do them both a lot of good and there was no medical reason why the pregnancy should not go ahead. I promised as much support as we could give but said I could not agree to termination.

After leaving me they went to another doctor who, although he felt as I did, reluctantly referred the wife to a gynaecologist on the grounds of her husband's anxiety.

The next thing I heard was that she was still pregnant. She told me that she could not bring herself to go through with an abortion. The result was a remarkably beautiful baby girl who, although she now merrily controls her parents, has done more for them than any tablets.

As one of my colleagues said, "There are few things more rewarding than watching a group of mums who have all been persuaded not to abort their babies happily comparing notes while their young roll around together on the floor."

Sometimes the decision to keep the baby requires a great deal of support. Fortunately organisations are springing up which offer this in most practical ways. The pressures to abort can come from many directions and in the first few weeks of pregnancy an emotionally upset woman is hardly in a state to come to a reasoned decision, though this is the right society is demanding for her.

One girl was being pressurised by her father to get rid of her baby while her mother was urging her not to. She was in a state of panic. Mother won and father stopped speaking to either of them. Halfway through the pregnancy her father came to see me. He was angry, depressed and not sleeping. His anger was mainly directed at the girl's boy-friend and his family, and he was feeling deeply the separation from his wife and daughter but dared not tell them so. I did my best to persuade him to accept the situation, but when the baby was born he refused to see it and the girl had to take it to her sister's home.

Some time later the girl told me that quite suddenly her father's attitude had changed. He had asked her to come home and was now the principal baby-worshipper. She and her boy-friend were to get married and her father had given his blessing.

The other day I heard of a girl who had an appointment with the abortion clinic but who wandered into the ante-natal clinic by mistake. The doctor, not knowing her mistake, examined her. When he had finished he said with a smile, "You're fine, the baby is fine and everything is going as it should." The girl was so taken aback that she found it impossible to go across the corridor to the other clinic. She now has a fine baby and is delighted.

I am alarmed by the easy acceptance of abortion as a reasonable way out of apparent problems or as an approved method of population control.

A young couple came together again after having

been separated. Shortly afterwards the wife became pregnant and as the husband had doubts about the wisdom of having another child at this point, they went to their doctor for advice. The doctor without hesitation recommended abortion and the wife was referred to a gynaecologist. Again she expected counselling, but after reading the GP's letter and examining her, the Registrar said, "Sure, if that's what you want, we'll do it for you." She apparently had not opened her mouth to say anything – people can still be in awe of doctors. By the time I met her she was feeling overwhelmed by grief and guilt. "Surely," she said, "the doctor should have known I wasn't the sort of person to want to go through with that. It was all too easily available. If it hadn't been, we'd have accepted the pregnancy and loved the baby."

Doctors are often asked to speak on subjects they may not know all that much about. On one occasion a vicar invited me to talk to a group of young people on the subject of adultery. He was taking them through the ten commandments and apparently thought that a doctor might cope better with "Thou shalt not commit adultery" than he. I foolishly accepted.

I expected a group of teenage girls, so was somewhat daunted to find a mixed group of about twenty-five. To make matters worse, staring at me from the front row was a handful of wide-eyed ten-year-old boys. They sat motionless during my twenty-minute talk, their eyes glued to my face. Afterwards they hung around on the edge of a circle of older girls who tried to push them away. When I finally got them on their own, their spokesman, after much nudging from his friends, blurted out with an endearing stammer, "We hate the way they are always going on about sex." He elaborated on the pornographic content of the Sunday press and television. "They even have it at tea-time when we are all watching," he added. The questions they asked revealed a burden of anxiety and half-knowledge which no ten-year-old should have to carry.

Sex can be a most demanding master. It is easily jealous, possessive and suspicious. It is also unforgiving.

One patient could not drop the subject of his wife's unfaithfulness many years previously. It kept him awake at night. He couldn't keep himself from taunting her with it, in spite of her regret and longing to make a success of their marriage both for their own sakes and for the sake of the children. She was ill and needing tranquillisers. He complained that the situation was affecting his efficiency at work, as much of his job involved delicate negotiations between people who found it difficult to agree with each other.

It is normal for us to want someone to love and to be loved by. Sex too is an essential part of our make-up and if God designed us then He must know how it is meant to be used and enjoyed. In a marriage where two people respect each other and have shared ideals and interests they need never be ruled by it or afraid of it.

Purity is a virtue rarely mentioned today. It

smacks of puritanism. Yet purity is, basically, no more than being free of the tyranny of our own lusts, something most of us would welcome with both hands. It is also concerned with a great deal more than overt sex.

Many of us know what it is like to be self-conscious, scared of meeting people we don't know or frightened to say what we think. Many of us know how it feels to be jealous or misunderstood. We may think we are not appreciated enough or feel rejected and left out in the cold.

My own experience is that when other people, and that includes my husband, become of more immediate importance to me than myself, then these paralysing demands fall away.

6

Dope and Teddy-Bears

From the day we are born we are dependent on someone or something. It only needs a short strike by refuse collectors or water workers to make us realise just how much we need each other. We come into a world in which we stand no chance of survival without the care of somebody, preferably our own parents. We need food, shelter and safety, but above all we need the emotional security which comes from being wanted. If this is lacking, however well-fed or well-housed we may be, we will have to turn somewhere else for help. A two-year-old, feeling pushed out by the advent of a new baby in the family, may grab a one-eared bear or a grubby blanket for comfort. On the other hand, a transformation comes over our small grandson when Grandpa stops shouting at him and goes off with him to hunt for fossils.

A child born into a home where it is wanted does not have to work at being accepted. It takes it for granted. Outside the home it is different. There we have to prove ourselves and how pleasant or unpleasant life is largely depends on whether we find ourselves included or left out.

There are characters who, if they are excluded, manage to shove themselves in. One bright thirteen-year-old told me, "I just shout a bit louder and they let me in." The less confident may feel badly battered. Two apparent alternatives seem open, to become a loner or to attempt to improve one's image.

With me it started at school where I was torn between wanting to be in the teachers' good books and wanting to be included in the popular gang who were usually in trouble. I allowed myself to be inveigled into one or two hazardous exploits but was in a state of terror all the time in case we should be caught. Popularity didn't seem worth the price so I settled for the friendship of another timid girl who had spots and greasy hair and with whom I really didn't want to be associated. I may say I also had spots and greasy hair and I dare say she felt the same way about me.

Mrs Gandhi once said in a television interview that every individual has resources within himself which should be sufficient to sustain him in times of stress. No one should have to depend on anyone else.

We are not all Mrs Gandhis. The vast majority of us represent the feebler and more vulnerable type of mortal. We cannot manage without support of some kind. What we decide to turn to will depend on our circumstances or our temperament.

The trouble is that nothing we turn to for support can be totally reliable. Whether it be drugs, food or alcohol we seem to need more and more. The best of human relationships may let us down. Some drugs, as is well-known, make us so physically dependent on them that our bodies react violently if they are suddenly withdrawn.

We once wrestled all night with a young man coming off heroin. We had been assured that he was already free of it, but, unknown to his family or the medical staff, a friend had been smuggling the drug in to him all the time he was in hospital being treated for the severe hepatitis which so often ends an addict's life. By the end of that first night, we were bruised and exhausted and had greatly broadened our vocabulary of four-letter words.

Vast numbers over the centuries have turned to alcohol. It remains the number one drug in the western world and is fast taking over elsewhere. In small amounts it aids digestion and may do something to safeguard against coronary artery disease but beyond that it is a "vicious poison", as Dr David Charley, until recently Consultant Chest Physician in Leeds, has described it. It destroys cells in the body, particularly in the brain and liver. After years of drinking a brain will shrink in size. Drinking during pregnancy causes defects in the developing embryo and leads to an undersized one.

People think of alcohol as a stimulant but this is an illusion. Even in very small doses alcohol depresses the higher centres in the brain which normally govern the way we behave, and in making us less inhibited makes us think we are relaxed. The shy person becomes talkative and the sense of self-importance is enhanced.

A report of the National Council of Women in 1976 pointed out that it takes very little alcohol, perhaps only half a pint of beer, to turn a quiet boy of twelve or thirteen into a vandal capable of doing hundreds of pounds' worth of damage. According to a Police Superintendent speaking at a conference in 1982, a recent survey showed a 32% rise in drunkenness offences of all sorts in the fourteen to seventeen age group. The NCW report also mentions the increase in the number of women who drink on their own at home.

The Wine and Spirit Association reports that during the last 25 years there has been a 50% rise in the consumption of beer; a 300% rise in consumption of spirits and a 600% rise in wine-drinking.

Most people will experiment with smoking, drinking, glue-sniffing or drugs during the growing-up period, some for the sake of being "one of the gang"; others, more adventurous, may just want to see what happens. But for many it is a more serious business. Two teenage girls told me that several of their friends at school, all under the legal age, drank quite regularly and often turned up at school with hangovers. I asked them why they thought they did it. "Well they all come from homes where the parents have split up," was their answer. A teacher underlined this by saying that alcohol now presented more of a problem in the school than sex. Two boys I knew took to drinking when their respective parents divorced. One was totally dependent by the time he was twenty.

One patient of ours was illegitimate and used to be left alone while his mother went out to work. At the age of three he was adopted by the keeper of a pub and his wife to replace a baby they had just lost through a miscarriage. There was an older sister who resented his arrival in the family. He was undernourished, and the GP suggested he should be given beer as there was plenty around.

At an early age he became involved with a gang which was constantly in trouble with the police. As he grew up his one solace was beer, and the only place in which he felt at home was a pub. To buy drink he had to steal. To give himself enough courage to steal he had to drink. So the vicious circle continued. The only time he felt he was any good was in an approved school where he was captain of the football team. As soon as he left he was on his own again. His greatest difficulty has been in accepting that anyone could ever be fond of him or need him.

It isn't only individuals who suffer. I remember hearing a North American Indian describe how his tribe was destroying itself with alcohol. He blamed this on the fact that they had been made to feel second-class citizens in their own country.

A young man came at intervals to get a prescription for acne. Eventually he told me he was a homosexual and was worried about his job which involved contact with boys. He felt inadequate and ashamed. To boost his confidence he had taken to drinking and was now alarmed at the control which this had over him. This further increased his poor opinion of himself and his isolation from his colleagues.

As he had been brought up in the Catholic Church, I suggested he should go back to this and take his beliefs seriously again. He agreed to do this and by the next time I saw him he was free of his homosexual urges. This had given him new confidence so he no longer needed to rely on alcohol. The threat to his job had been removed.

A lady with all that money could buy had a row with her mother over some family business. Her mother, a dominating character, swore violently at her and finally disowned her. From that day she started drinking secretly with disastrous effects on her family life.

On a particular day, at my husband's suggestion, several small groups of her friends got together in different places to pray for her and her mother. She described afterwards how she had experienced a sudden feeling of release. From that day she no longer felt any need to go on drinking. Later she and her mother were reconciled.

In my area the problems of drugs and glue-sniffing are not yet finding their way into many GP's surgeries. They are more often dealt with in the casualty departments of hospitals or in special clinics. Their rarity in the surgery means they may be missed.

A girl came to the surgery who had been seriously disturbed after seeing a film about the Devil. She had expected the effects of it to wear off

after a time, but instead she was haunted more and
more and would wake in the night and "see" the
Devil. "I know what he looks like," she said. It was
as though a voice inside her was telling her she was
no use and should destroy herself. The sad thing
was that she didn't know how to tell anyone what
she was going through. She was not eating and had
lost weight. Eventually she had plucked up courage
to see a doctor.

It was obvious that tranquillisers by themselves
would not help much and there was no evidence of
psychiatric illness. I told her this and that I felt the
only way to deal with that kind of trouble was to tell
God about it and ask Him to help. To my surprise
she agreed with alacrity, so we prayed together there
and then. She went off very happily. Some months
later her mother came to see me. She told me her
daughter was fine and that she had stopped taking
drugs the day she saw me. This remark shook me as
on that occasion I had quite failed to take the possibility of drugs into account.

I once found myself involved with a case of drug-
taking without ever meeting the patient. His mother
came to see me in a very disturbed state. She was
becoming increasingly anxious about her husband
whom she suspected of having an affair with
someone else, refusing to believe that it was simply
arduous new job responsibilities that kept him out
late and made him reluctant to talk when he came
home. Meanwhile he was finding her attitude so
difficult that he was seriously thinking of leaving her.

On direct questioning my patient said she had

started drinking heavily when she was alone at home. Later it came out that she was also worried about her nineteen-year-old son who had left home after being refused work by his father and had got in with a group who took drugs and stole to pay for them. He was due to appear in court on a drugs charge. She had plenty to disturb her sleep and give her bad dreams.

I suggested that she might try taking time each morning to pray for her husband and son and ask God to speak to her about how she herself could be different. She was not used to praying, but she decided to make the experiment. In a very short time her depression lifted and with it her suspicions. I had told her I could not treat her unless she stopped drinking and she did this too.

A few weeks later her son phoned and she told him she had been praying for him. "I've found myself praying too," he said. "I've never done it before and I never thought I would." The court case came and his honesty and determination not to touch drugs again led to a minimal punishment. His father asked him to come home and offered him a job in his business. One day my patient jokingly asked her husband whether he ever now thought of leaving home. "Yes, my love," he said. "Every morning when I go to work."

One day while the young heroin addict was recovering in our home, he suddenly disappeared. I was sure he had gone off to look for drugs in the nearby town. Feeling quite desperate, I found myself saying again and again, "Lead us not into temptation."

It was the first time that sentence in the Lord's Prayer had meant anything to me. Half an hour later he telephoned to say he'd had such a "hell of a time" on the bus that he'd got off halfway to town and was coming straight back.

Many parents say how difficult it is to control their young and prevent them from harming themselves by getting into bad habits. This reminds me of a sketch I once saw performed in which a man was holding forth on the evils of society in general and of youth in particular. He spoke in learned terms about vandalism, sex and drug addiction. All the while he was holding a bottle in one hand and a lighted cigarette in the other, from which he took alternate swigs and puffs. The longer he talked the more slurred his speech became and the more vehement he waxed. Finally as he staggered off the stage he said with a gesture of hopelessness, "I can't understand why it is that the young don't want to take our advice."

Frequent visitors to the surgery are the women who want to lose weight. There is only one way to get fat and that is to eat more than the body can make use of. This amount varies greatly from person to person, so that some people get fat far more quickly than others. There may be medicial reasons for this. For example, a patient with an underactive thyroid gland will readily put on weight while another with an overactive gland will continue to lose weight whatever she eats.

Overeating is only too common among those of us in our affluent society whose glands function normally. We may eat for the sheer delight of it. Where there is a compulsion to eat, however, diagnosis of the underlying reason is essential if dieting is to achieve lasting results. I know from my own experience that food can become as much of a dependence as alcohol or tobacco.

Being alone, bored, uncertain what to do next, dissatisfied or disgruntled are all incentives to fill oneself up with food. My strongest urge to eat usually came on evenings when my husband was out and I was left alone with the sleeping children and a full fridge.

At one point one of our children took to helping herself to food from the larder. When I was wondering what to do about this, I had a vivid picture of myself doing precisely the same thing. As mother I thought I had a right to eat when I liked, but when I stopped she stopped too. Identifying with others with similar problems to one's own is a great aid to self-discipline.

One young mother asked me for tablets to help her to lose weight. She suffered from "bulimia" – she would stuff herself with food, often with food she disliked, and then make herself sick. She, as well as I, felt there must be some reason for this strange behaviour. She then told me she had been adopted when she was only a few months old and had never known her own family. She had grown up very happily in her adopted family but always at the back of her mind was the feeling that she was "the cause of all the trouble". We imagined that quite possibly her unplanned arrival had caused upheavals in the family and that grandmother had blamed her. Whatever the actual truth might be, she decided she would start praying for her mother and grandmother.

The next time she came she told me she had felt she should also include her father, about whom she knew absolutely nothing. A month or so later she said she felt that the whole of her natural family had been "lifted out" of her life and that she need not be burdened by them any more. The feeling of blame had gone and so had the compulsion to eat. She began to feel she was a person in her own right regardless of her family background. She still had occasional lapses when she felt she had caused trouble to someone but as soon as she had talked out her worries, the problem vanished once more.

Even when people accept the need to lose weight it is difficult to convince them on the matter of diet. I called unexpectedly at teatime on an elderly woman who was supposed to be dieting for the sake of her heart, only to find her gorging her second cream bun. She was quite unabashed by my rebuke. She thought it was quite all right to eat cream buns as long as she took her diet at regular intervals as well.

Dependence on the good opinion of others may make us conform to what we imagine they expect of us.

As a student I particularly wanted to be liked by a certain girl. She and her friends were all seasoned smokers. My reason told me that smoking, for me at least, was an expensive and unproductive habit but at the same time that it was desirable if I was to avoid feeling self-conscious and inferior in their company.

So I rather miserably and amateurishly smoked too. Far from giving me confidence it only made me feel more inadequate, as I knew my motives were shoddy. When I finally decided to stop and announce that I was a non-smoker, my confidence was restored and I unexpectedly found myself accepted as perfectly normal.

A friend of mine had a daughter in the sixth form at the local school. One day the girl came home and announced that it was her turn to have a bottle party. My friend was also told that she would be expected to go out that evening. It was quite out of character for the girl to order her mother about like this and she was hardly surprised when mother said that she and her father would not want them drinking in the house. The girl retorted that no one would want to come to a party without alcohol and went off to school banging the front door behind her.

Mother was left wondering how on earth to handle the situation. Finally she decided to refer the matter to God and by the time her daughter came home again she felt quite ready to cope. She said that everyone would be very welcome but there would be no alcohol and she had no intention of going out. It was her home and she wanted to make sure they all had a good time. The daughter shrugged and reluctantly agreed. "But of course none of them will come now," she said.

However, when the evening arrived, about twelve turned up, each armed with a bottle of soft drink. My friend welcomed them and told them to make themselves at home. There were mince-pies in the kitchen and they could make coffee if they wanted it. She then settled down in the sitting room to play Scrabble with a friend who had dropped in for an hour.

When she saw her friend off, there was absolute silence in the rest of the house. Wondering what she would find, she went upstairs. Her daughter's bedroom door was shut and there was no sound from inside. With some trepidation she opened it. There they all were. They had raided the old toy cupboard and pulled out all the games. Three six-footers were lying on the floor, their hands over their eyes, trying to get fish out of a cardboard pond with magnets on strings. Others lay sprawled around playing games or reading books. They were all too occupied to notice her. She left the room and closed the door.

At ten-thirty the daughter came down to ask how much longer they could stay and mother suggested another half hour. Punctually at eleven o'clock they knocked on the sitting-room door and came in to shake hands with mother. They thanked her for a "super" evening and later on they told the daughter that it was the best evening they'd had. After they had gone mother found the mince-pies had vanished and all the washing up had been done and put away. Several parents told her how grateful they were for what she had done.

What people thought meant a great deal to me. This reached a climax when I was stranded in Calcutta waiting for a boat to take me on to China. I was staying in the bishop's house and sharing a bedroom with two girls who were working in India. Because of the war, the shipping lines could give no information about ships' movements, and when no boat turned up, I began to wonder whether God was trying to stop me for some reason. Maybe He didn't want me to go to China and marry Ken after all – we were still not officially engaged. Although neither of my friends had said anything about it, I began to imagine that they were thinking the same thing. As I thought about it I found myself in more and more of a turmoil. Should I stop now? If I did, what would my family think? What would the Missionary Society think? Above all, what would Ken do? If I stuck to my original plan what would my new friends think? It is often those closest at hand whose opinions matter most.

At this point one of my friends, aware that something was wrong, invited me into the bathroom adjoining the bedroom, where we could be quiet and undisturbed. Her idea was to give God a chance to talk to me. There I sat on a hard chair gazing at a palm tree outside the window. After a few moments my friend got up and left the room, closing the door behind her. I knew I dare not leave that bathroom until I had decided, not so much what I should do at that moment, but whether from that time on I was going to care only about what God thought of me, rather than floundering about in my dependence on everyone else.

It took the best part of three hours to reach what I knew must be an honest decision. I knew that once I had agreed to put God first in my life, I must be

prepared for anything He might tell me to do. To
turn my back on China and Ken was obviously the
most difficult thing He might ask of me. Finally I said
"Yes" to God. At once I felt as though chains had
fallen off me and I was free. I also knew without any
doubt that it was right for me to go ahead with my
plans. Neither of my friends asked any questions
and neither seemed in the least concerned about my
decision to go on. They just seemed pleased that I
was different. The next day the shipping line phoned
to say that a boat had arrived.

In spite of the uncomfortable and often
frightening things which followed this experience, I
have known since that time that God is all I need to
depend on. I can count on Him to be there to turn
to at any time. With the realisation that He can be
concerned about me and my doings comes the
certainty that He is equally concerned about
everyone else. It is impossible to undervalue anyone
on that basis.

7

To Be Taken . . .

The fascinating thing about general practice is that one never knows who is going to walk in through the surgery door next, or what sort of problem they will bring with them. It may be an old man or a toddler, a schoolmistress or the small boy she teaches. It may be a stevedore, a parson or a refuse collector. The patient may be black, yellow or white. He may live in a beautiful house or have no home at all. He may be suffering from any disease in the textbook.

The great majority come with run-of-the-mill complaints, sore throats, varicose veins or ingrowing toenails. But one always has to be on the alert for something more serious or unusual. An old professor used to say to us, "If you see a bird sitting on a tree, it is probably a sparrow but it just might be a canary." A routine test may reveal unexpectedly that a patient has diabetes. In the same way a casual question such as "Is everything else all right?" thrown in at the end of a straightforward consultation, may unleash a flood of tears, and the story of some problem which the patient had no intention of talking about. One wonders just how much lies bottled up inside people, waiting to be released like the pus in an infected finger.

Often patients come with their own diagnosis. The other day a lady told me, "I know it's my stomach because of my eyes." I am still trying to work that one out.

Sometimes it is somebody else's diagnosis. On one occasion a woman booked in for a ten-minute appointment and then told me very confidentially, "I haven't come about myself but about your next patient. I thought you would like to know," – in a hushed voice – "it's her liver." When her friend came in I had great difficulty in getting her liver out of my mind, although there was nothing to suggest there was anything wrong with it.

Occasionally it's the "sparrow" which is unexpected. An old man came to see my husband one day complaining that his sight was getting very bad. Ken removed the man's glasses, breathed on them and gave them a good wipe with his handkerchief and the patient's sight was restored.

It can be embarrassing when patients know more about a new drug or line of treatment than I do because I haven't read the Sunday newspaper or watched a particular television programme. It used to be thought poor practice to look up anything in front of the patient but there are so many new products these days that it is impossible to know them all.

Fear of an alarming diagnosis may keep patients away from their doctors. One of my patients found a lump in her breast and was secretly sure she had cancer but too scared to find out. She lived with her fear for months. When she did consult me it was only a harmless cyst. But there is always the danger that, through fear, a patient may leave something until it is too late to treat.

Others fear their doctor's reaction if nothing is found to be wrong. They are often profuse in their apologies for having wasted our time. They don't realise that it is almost as much relief to the doctor as it is to the patient when all is well.

We hear a great deal about patients visiting their doctors with trivial complaints. I have found that if a person feels the need to go to a doctor, they always have a genuine problem, although it may not be the one they produce first. There may be underlying fear, made worse by having no one to talk to. Very often the doctor is the only person they can think of to consult, and as fear or unhappiness are quite capable of producing headaches or sleeplessness, they have a legitimate excuse.

What is trivial to one person may be vital to another.

A young Australian came to the surgery one day complaining of pain in her hand which she said she had injured in the washing machine. There was no sign of injury. Her fingers all moved freely and there was no swelling. All I could find was a small area of tenderness. She seemed to be making a fuss about very little.

As she talked it emerged she was a professional violinist and was genuinely afraid that her hand might get worse and affect her playing. I still thought she was unduly anxious. Then she told me that her husband had died after only a few months of marriage and she had come to Britain to get over her bereavement. So here she was in a strange country, knowing few people and trying to rebuild her life.

Time is a great factor in a GP's life. How much can you achieve in ten minutes or less? One irate lady spent the first half of her precious appointment complaining that she had been kept waiting for thirty-five minutes. When she stopped talking, I asked her how long she would like me to spend with her. She laughed and said, "Yes, that's different, isn't it?"

Fortunately many patients can be adequately dealt with in the allotted time. More time spent today on those who need it may save time on another day. Everyone, whatever their complaint, deserves the same concern. This is not always easy to remember.

I ushered a rather scruffy old man into the surgery one evening wishing I didn't have to be bothered with him. As we both sat down, I felt God was saying to me, "I'm only asking you to care for him." It suddenly seemed a very small thing to do for someone. As he talked I found him unexpectedly alert and interesting. He told me how his faith in God had kept him going through many difficult years. We parted like old friends and I felt better for having seen him.

As well as the medical challenge, general practice provides fascinating scraps of information about one's patients' lives. Some of this comes out in conversation between an over-talkative patient and an over-inquisitive doctor. One learns what it is like to spend hours looking through binoculars at minute electrical circuits or crawling around sweating inside a ship's boiler, that firemen often suffer from excessive cold through getting wet, and how much of their free time union officials spend looking after the social needs of their members.

Most information emerges because it is relevant to the person's illness or their treatment. A building worker's hernia will need repairing more urgently than an office clerk's and he will need longer convalescence. It is no good sending a policeman back on the beat if his feet still hurt. A man who has giddy turns might return to his desk, but certainly should not be allowed to shin up and down vertical ladders at an oil refinery.

Above all one learns about people's homes and their communities. Mrs S came to the surgery one day in a state of great distress because she was sleeping badly. A new neighbour, who worked in a nightclub with her daughters, had moved into the other half of her semi-detached house a few months before. Every night Mrs S would be woken by the sound of banging doors and a record player being turned on full blast on the other side of her thin bedroom walls. As she had no other bedroom into which she could escape, she either had to bury her head under the pillow or set out on the road of protest. The pillow was quite inadequate and she hadn't much faith in protest. Anyway she hated having rows with people.

Could I just give her a sleeping tablet strong enough to make her oblivious to it all?

I knew from previous encounters that she believed in God so I suggested that He might have another way of dealing with the situation. She was willing to consider this, a trifle doubtfully. We began to talk about the neighbour and how difficult she must find it to cope with a night job and with looking after her home and growing-up daughters without the support of a husband. Mrs S brightened up at this point. Perhaps she should try to get to know her neighbour better. Up to now she had not even wanted to speak to her.

A few days later Mrs S called in next door and asked whether there were any odd jobs she could do, like shopping, which might make things easier. Then she started leaving the occasional vegetable on the neighbour's doorstep. Meanwhile she went on taking the sleeping tablets. A week or two later the neighbour asked her over the garden fence whether, by any chance, she ever heard them when they came in at night. She had been so kind that they would hate to think they were disturbing her. Mrs S admitted that she did get woken up. The noise stopped forthwith and she slept peacefully once more.

I was not always ready to bring God into my conversations with patients. "They might not like it and one should be very careful," I told myself. I thought it wise that they should approve of me before I ventured into such deep waters.

Many years ago an Indian businessman, who

was visiting Britain, came to see me. While he was walking along the beach at a seaside resort he had been accosted by a girl who had invited him back to her flat. He thought this must be normal British hospitality and that it would be rude to refuse. Now he was convinced that he had caught some nasty disease from her and was quite terrified by the thought. There was no evidence that he was ill. I wanted to help him realise that God could take away his fear and felt it was my duty to do so, but I did not want to rush him. So I arranged for a series of injections, one a day for the next six days, hoping that by the end I would have gained his confidence sufficiently to get my message across. With each injection the subject seemed more difficult to introduce and I never got round to it. He went away somewhat relieved, but still unhappy and with a poor opinion of Britain.

As my own certainty has grown that what everyone needs most is the knowledge that there is a God who cares, forgives and can change us, I have become bolder. I have also learned that though you may ask a patient to come back, they often don't. Now if I hesitate it is not because of my reputation but because of the time and effort which may be needed if I decide to get involved with a patient's problems. In fact, as soon as I take the plunge, a completely different quality of concern for the person facing me takes over. Then, always to my surprise, the necessary questions or suggestions come into my mind, the real problem emerges and the time taken is often less than I was expecting.

What has surprised me is not the scorn or oppo-
sition which I have expected when God is mentioned,
but the sense of relief in the most unexpected people.
It is almost as though they were saying, "Thank
goodness someone is ready to talk about Him." I can
only think of one girl who tossed her beautiful long-
haired head and said, "Oh, Him! Nobody bothers to
think about Him these days." Even she looked
pensive when I remarked that fortunately this made
no difference to the way He thought about her.

It is moving to discover how many people still
pray, often secretly, or slip into a church on a
weekday when no one is around, because of the
peace they find there. I get the impression that there
are very few who do not believe at least enough to
say, "Help!" when in trouble.

An eight-year-old girl was brought in by her
father one day. "She has had a tummy-ache for two
years," he said aggressively. "The school says something's got to be done about it." I looked through
her notes and found she had been thoroughly inves-
tigated and there seemed very little left for me to
do. As children are often more articulate when their
parents are not present, I asked the father to leave
us alone. Then I asked her why she thought she
had tummy-aches. "I sometimes wonder whether it's
because I'm always scared," was her rather surprising answer. She was scared, so it seemed, of almost
everything. She imagined witches looking in at her
bedroom window and unknown horrors lurking
behind the bathroom door. This, incidentally, may
have accounted for some of the tummy-aches, as

she avoided going there whenever she could. Even children's television was "scary".

I asked her whether she ever said prayers. "Oh yes," she answered, "because we do in Brownies." "Do your Mummy and Daddy ever say their prayers?" I asked. "I don't think so," she said doubtfully. She had clearly never discussed such things with them. Then she said, as she twisted around in her chair, "I often want to ask God to speak to me, because you know, He used to talk to people in the Bible. But then, I think, supposing He did," and she curled right up in her chair, "what would happen?"

I told her she wasn't the first person to think this, but that in fact I wanted Him to speak to me too, and when He did it wasn't frightening at all. He just put thoughts into my head about what to do and made me feel He was very close. I thought of Him as my best friend. I told her that she could think of Him as Jesus because Jesus wasn't frightening and that is how we know God best. She could talk to Him at any time about anything. He would always look after her and she need never be scared again.

When her father came back into the room, I gave him a prescription for a vitamin syrup, partly to satisfy him but mainly because I thought it might improve her appetite, as she was certainly a bit skinny.

Several weeks later they were both back with one of the other children who had a sore throat. The eight-year-old looked fine. "That was an excellent syrup you gave her," said father. I looked at the small figure with her straight hair and National

Health glasses and she looked back at me with a serene expression on her face. "Any more tummy-aches?" I asked. "No," she said. "Any more scary things?" "No," she said, with a decided shake of her head. I felt pretty sure it had taken more than the syrup to cure her.

We decided long ago that the most important contribution we could make to the welfare of our family was not advice or pocket money but the time we devoted each morning to referring the day to God and asking for His control and direction in it. It can be difficult on a cold, dark morning or when children are climbing over you, but God seems to honour the most struggling efforts to get in touch with Him. It is important that this time should not be hurried. For us it has become more important than breakfast, though we don't often miss that either.

It is often said that doctors should never impose their moral or religious ideas upon their patients. This is similar to the view that religious education should not be given in schools – children should be free to make up their own minds when they grow up. But how can people choose if the choice is never presented to them? In medicine we try to keep up with the latest and best treatment available. We know about antibiotics now so it would be a crime not to use them when necessary. Patients themselves are very ready to ask for some drug which has helped a friend with a similar complaint. If I know of thousands of people, including myself, for whom faith in God has provided new health and hope, is it right that I should keep quiet about it and refuse to offer it?

Quite apart from rights and wrongs, it is impossible for doctors, or anyone else, not to pass on something of their attitude to life and the values they hold. It will show in everything they do or say.

Of course a patient has every right to accept or reject our advice. It is often difficult enough to ensure that a patient takes the full course of treatment. Doctors themselves are as bad as anyone else in this respect. The moment patients feel a bit better, they stop the tablets without consulting their doctor and then back they come with a recurrence of the complaint.

Some go even further. One old lady would summon me urgently to the hotel in which she lived. On each occasion she would tell me she was no better. Each time I would find her bottle of tablets untouched in her bedside cupboard. She treated my remonstrations as a huge joke.

One woman complained about an irritating cough. Asked about her smoking habits she readily admitted to having smoked forty or more cigarettes a day for years. When I suggested she would do well to give them up she just laughed. "Just give me something to relieve the cough," she said, "that's all I want." She didn't want her chest examined and she certainly did not want me to find out why she needed to smoke so heavily. The thought of a life crippled by chronic bronchitis or early death from lung cancer did not seem to concern her.

We tend to have the same approach to spiritual

medicine. One friend of mine gives time to thinking about God when she feels out of sorts, but the moment she feels better she stops. Then she wonders why the problems mount up again. Another woman was enthusiastic about the idea of giving God a chance to run the world His way, but said that she was far too busy at the moment to consider it properly. She would look into it more when she had time. That was two years ago and she still hasn't had enough time.

Such reactions remind me of the small boy down whose severely inflamed throat I was trying to pour a spoonful of antibiotic while his mother struggled to hold him still. "I'm too ill to take my medicine," he bellowed as the tears ran down his red cheeks, "I'll take it when I'm better."

It took four years to persuade one woman to try it out. During that time she must have consumed hundreds of tablets to ease her anxiety. Then one day she came into my room and said, "I haven't come because I'm ill. I just wanted you to know that I have discovered that I can talk to God or listen to Him at any time of day or night. I never thought this could happen to me." Since then she has come through experiences that would have floored the most stout-hearted. As well as this, her husband began asking her advice about problems at work which he had never discussed with her before.

In this divided, violent, starvation-ridden world, the need for new ways of doing things must be obvious to the dullest of us. Politicians can't be expected to produce miracles on their own. Violent revolution is unlikely to produce lasting results as it only replaces one lot who think they know how to run things with another lot who think precisely the same. Increasing permissiveness only makes for more and more self-centred people.

It may seem naïve to call for change in individuals but to expect a radical permanent change in society without it is to expect the impossible. The kind of change which God offers us is a medicine with nothing but good side-effects. It costs only our pride and self-will and is cheap at the price. It may appear hard to swallow at first but as the effects become apparent it gets easier to take. People who take it regularly find that selfish characters can become unselfish; that marriages can not only last but get richer as time goes on; that anxiety can be replaced by tranquillity, bitterness and hate by forgiveness and love; and that an empty life can become full.